Anthony Lenarski

## Butterfly Books

in the same series:

HIDDEN IN THE MEADOW
HIDDEN BY THE POND
the butterfly book of MAMMALS
the butterfly book of BIRDS
PLAINS INDIANS of North America
IN MY GARDEN (learning to count)
THE FOUR SEASONS
LITTLE RED RIDING HOOD

## TWO CONTINENTS

*Anne-Marie Dalmais*

*Benvenuti*

# THE 3 BEARS

Once upon a time there were three bears: Papa Bear, Mama Bear and Baby Bear. They lived in a cottage at the far end of the forest. One morning, a very curious little girl named Goldilocks, taking a walk in the forest, found the cottage and peeped in the window. The three bears were away, so she went right in and made herself at home.

On the table she saw three bowls of porridge. Goldilocks tasted them all. The first one was too hot. The second one was too cold. The third was just right. Goldilocks ate it all up!

She saw three chairs. She sat in them one after the other, and liked the smallest one best. But when she thumped down into it, it broke to pieces!

Goldilocks ran upstairs. In the bedroom she bounced on each of the beds, feet first. "It's the best way", she said to herself, "to find the most comfortable bed". The first one was too hard. The second one was too soft. The third one was just right, and Goldilocks lay down and went to sleep.

The three bears came back from their walk.

"Somebody's been eating my porridge", growled Papa Bear. "Somebody's been eating my porridge", said Mama Bear.
"Somebody's been eating my porridge and ate it all up!" Baby Bear cried.

Then they saw the chairs. "Somebody's been sitting in my chair", roared Papa Bear. "Somebody's been sitting in my chair", said Mama Bear. "Somebody's been sitting in my chair and broke it to pieces!" cried Baby Bear.

The bears ran upstairs. "Somebody's been jumping on my bed!" roared Papa Bear. "Somebody's been jumping on my bed", said Mama Bear. "Somebody's been sleeping in my bed", cried Baby Bear, "and HERE SHE IS!"

Goldilocks woke up. In a fright, she jumped out of the window and ran away. The three bears never saw her again.

This charming book also comes in a poster version, ready to brighten a child's wall.  Your bookseller has it as well as others of the series.

illustration
Benvenuti

text
Anne-Marie Dalmais

adaptation
Robert Maguire

design
Michel Cartacheff

Butterfly Books

**TWO CONTINENTS PUBLISHING GROUP**
30 East 42 Street, New York, New York 10017

Months of the Year

# June

by Robyn Brode

Reading consultant: Susan Nations, M.Ed.,
author/literacy coach/consultant

WEEKLY WR READER®
EARLY LEARNING LIBRARY

Please visit our web site at: **www.earlyliteracy.cc**
**For a free color catalog describing Weekly Reader® Early Learning Library's list of high-quality books, call 1-877-445-5824 (USA) or 1-800-387-3178 (Canada). Weekly Reader® Early Learning Library's fax: (414) 336-0164.**

**Library of Congress Cataloging-in-Publication Data**

Brode, Robyn.
    June / by Robyn Brode.
      p. cm. — (Months of the year)
    Summary: An introduction to some of the characteristics, events, and activities
of the month of June.
    ISBN 0-8368-3581-6 (lib. bdg.)
    ISBN 0-8368-3617-0 (softcover)
    1. June (Month)—Juvenile literature.  2. Holidays—United States—Juvenile literature.
[1. June (Month).]  I. Title.
GT4803.B768   2003
394.263—dc21                        2002034313

First published in 2003 by
**Weekly Reader® Early Learning Library**
330 West Olive Street, Suite 100
Milwaukee, WI 53212 USA

Editor: Robyn Brode
Art direction, design, and page production: Leonardo Montenegro with Orange Avenue
Models: Olivia Byers-Strans, Isabella Leary, Madeline Leary
Weekly Reader® Early Learning Library art direction: Tammy Gruenewald
Weekly Reader® Early Learning Library editor: Mark J. Sachner

Photo credits: Cover, title, pp. 7, 9, 13, 15, 17, 21 © Getty Images; pp. 11, 19
Leonardo Montenegro

Printed in the United States of America

1 2 3 4 5 6 7 8 9 07 06 05 04 03

# Note to Educators and Parents

Reading is such an exciting adventure for young children! They are beginning to integrate their oral language skills with written language. To help this process along, books must be meaningful, colorful, engaging, and interesting; they should invite young readers to make inquiries about the world around them.

*Months of the Year* is a new series of books designed to help children learn more about each of the twelve months. In each book, young readers will learn about festivals, celebrations, weather, and other interesting facts about each month.

Each book is specially designed to support the young reader in the reading process. The familiar topics are appealing to young children and invite them to re-read — again and again. The full-color photographs and enhanced text further support the student during the reading process.

These books are designed to be read within an instructional guided reading group. This small group setting allows beginning readers to work with a fluent adult model as they make meaning from the text. After children develop fluency with the text and content, the book can be read independently. Children and adults alike will find these books supportive, engaging, and fun!

— *Susan Nations, M.Ed., author, literacy coach, and consultant in literacy development*

June is the sixth month of the year. June has 30 days.

# June

**6**

| | | | | | | |
|---|---|---|---|---|---|---|
| 1 | 2 | 3 | 4 | 5 | 6 | 7 |
| 8 | 9 | 10 | 11 | 12 | 13 | 14 |
| 15 | 16 | 17 | 18 | 19 | 20 | 21 |
| 22 | 23 | 24 | 25 | 26 | 27 | 28 |
| 29 | 30 | | | | | |

In June, spring ends and summer begins. Summer usually begins on June 21.

When summer begins,
the days are the longest.
It is light for a much
longer time than it is dark.

In June it is warm and sunny. In places where it is very warm, sunflowers can grow tall in the sun.

*Do sunflowers grow where you live?*

The third Sunday in June is Father's Day. Kids give cards and gifts to dads and other men who are important to them.

In some places, school ends in June. Friends like to make summer plans together.

It is fun to celebrate the end of school. Sometimes classmates go to an amusement park for a whole day.

Sometimes classmates have picnics outdoors. Pizza is a favorite food for a picnic — and any other time!

*What do you like to do at the end of school?*

When June ends, it is time for July to begin.

# Glossary

**amusement park** — a place that has lots of fast rides and games to play

**Father's Day** — a special day to thank Dad and other men who are important to us

**summer** — a season that begins on the day it stays light longest

# Months of the Year

| | | | |
|---|---|---|---|
| 1 | January | 7 | July |
| 2 | February | 8 | August |
| 3 | March | 9 | September |
| 4 | April | 10 | October |
| 5 | May | 11 | November |
| 6 | **June** | 12 | December |

# Seasons of the Year

| | |
|---|---|
| Winter | Summer |
| Spring | Fall |

## About the Author

**Robyn Brode** wrote the *Going Places* children's book series and was the editor for *Get Out!*, which won the 2002 Disney Award for Hands-On Activities. She has been an editor, writer, and teacher in the book publishing field for many years. She earned a Bachelors in English Literature from the University of California at Berkeley.